It is recommended that adults and older kids help younger children with the directions for papercrafts.

 Page numbers on the stars tell you where to find objects described in the directions below.

Materials:
- markers or crayons
- glue stick and tape
- ribbon

CARDS AND GIFT TAGS
pages 1-2

CARDS
1. Press out the two Christmas cards.

2. Color each card, write your message on the back, add a postcard stamp and an address, and send it to a friend (figure 1).

GIFT TAGS
1. Press out the four gift tags.

2. Color the pictures. After TO: write the name of the person the gift is for. After FROM: write your own name. Decorate the back of each gift tag with stickers if you wish. Attach the gift tags to your gifts with some pretty ribbon (figure 2).

CHARACTERS
pages 3-4

1. Press out the four different cut-out characters.

2. Color them on the back. You can decorate them with stickers, too!

3. Add a loop of ribbon to each character, so that you can hang them on the Christmas tree (figure 1).

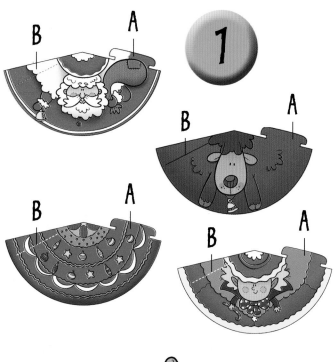

pages 5-6

CONES

1. Press out all the pieces from the pages. Fold along the dotted lines.

2. Color them on the back. You can add stickers if you wish. Decide if you want your colored side or the pre-printed side facing out.

3. Slide flap A into slot B (figure 1) to form a cone. Add a piece of tape on the inside to help hold your cone together. Push the reindeer's antlers into the slots on either side of its head (figure 2).

4. Use your cones as table decorations or tape on a loop of ribbon and hang them on the Christmas tree.

pages 7-8

DECORATIONS

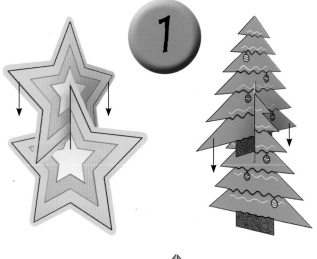

1. Carefully press out all the pieces from the pages.

2. Color them on the back.

3. To make the star and Christmas tree, slot each of the two identical halves together as shown (figure 1).

4. Use these as table decorations (figure 2).

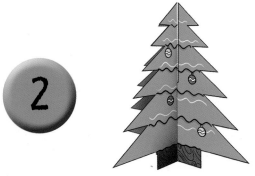

TO: ---------------------------------

FROM: -------------------------------

TO: ---------------------------------

FROM: -------------------------------

TO: ---------------------------------

FROM: -------------------------------

TO: ---------------------------------

FROM: -------------------------------

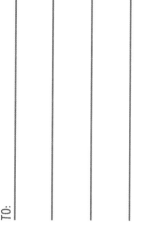

TO:

TO: